COMMON LIFE ON THE SEASHORE
OF THE CHANNEL ISLANDS

by

Gene Rowe

Illustrated by

Wendy Bramall

· 1995
published by La Société Guernesiaise
Candie Gardens, St Peter Port, Guernsey, GY1 1UG

First published 1995

ISBN 0-9518075-4-4

TABLE OF CONTENTS

FOREWORD

The seashore around the Channel islands has a very rich flora and fauna with many kinds of habitats on the shore, e.g. sandy, rocky, under stones or weed, in pools, crevices etc. This richness is increased because of the high tidal range due to the geographical position of the islands in the Gulf of St Malo. This causes large areas of shore to be exposed at low tide, providing a splendid hunting ground for those interested in life on the seashore.

This book has been written by Gene Rowe who was for a number of years the Secretary of the Marine Biology Section of La Société Guernesiaise. The illustrations are by Wendy Bramall, a well-known illustrator of Natural History books, who is also a member of La Société Guernesiaise.

It has been designed specifically for amateur islanders and visitors as well as for children, many of whom enjoy pottering about on the seashore. No attempt has been made to cover anything but the obvious. Those able to find most of the 64 species listed should not find it too difficult to go on and to handle the many field guides that are available from most bookshops. A list of these is below. A X10 hand lens is a useful aid.

ACKNOWLEDGEMENTS

The author would like to acknowledge the help and encouragement given in the preparation of this book by Jean Carré, Marie Mendham, Pat Sauvarin, Roger Brehaut, Griff Caldwell, Joan Bagley and Michael Romeril.

REFERENCE BOOKS

Books recommended by the author for those who wish to increase their knowledge of life on the shore are:
The Country Life Guide to the Seashore and Shallow Seas of Britain and Europe by A. C. Campbell.
Collins' Pocket Guide to the Seashore by J. Barrett & C. M. Yonge.
The Sea Shore by C. M. Yonge.
The Living Shore by Joan M. Clayton.
The Seashore, in the Collins Gem Guide series.
All books on Shore Life by Heather Angel, published by Jarrold & Sons Ltd.

TIDES

There are two high and two low tides in approximately twenty-four hours. The rise and fall of the tides depend on the movement of the earth and moon. They can be predicted accurately and are published each year in tide-tables, available from most book shops and chandlers.

A spring tide is when the rise and fall is at a maximum. It occurs fortnightly at the time of full and new moons. The neap tide is when there is least rise and fall and occurs mid-way between spring tides. Hence not only are there numerous habitats on the shore but the animal and plant life survives at varying levels, according to their tolerance of exposure, e.g. animals at the top half of the shore will be exposed twice a day to both summer and winter temperatures, whereas animals at extreme low water will only be exposed for a short period on a few days each month. Therefore, the zones are often very well defined, especially on rocky shores where the bands of different kinds of seaweeds can easily be seen.

Due to the geographical position of the Channel islands there is a greater rise and fall of the tides than those in most places on the other side of the Channel. As an example at high spring tides in Jersey the difference between high and low tide can reach over 12 metres or about 40 feet. At similar tides in Guernsey the figures are slightly less, being nearly 10 metres or 33 feet.

WARNING

The tide takes roughly six hours to rise from low to high tide. During that time it will rise at high spring tides as much as 40 feet in six hours in Jersey, or over 30 feet in six hours in Guernsey. This is equivalent to over six feet an hour in Jersey or about five feet an hour in Guernsey. It is very easy on warm summer's day to become so interested in a rock pool that one does not notice the incoming tide and so can become cut off.

DO WATCH OUT FOR THE RISING TIDE
WHEN POTTERING ON THE SEASHORE

INTRODUCTION

Most of the animals mentioned in this book will generally be found in a particular zone on the seashore. The division of the seashore into zones depends entirely on the rise and fall of the tides. This is best illustrated diagrammatically as can be seen below.

DIVISION OF SEASHORE INTO ZONES

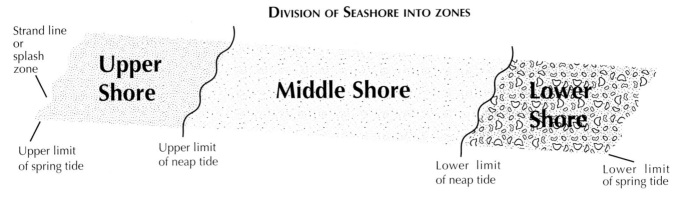

Strand line or splash zone

Upper limit of spring tide

Upper limit of neap tide

Lower limit of neap tide

Lower limit of spring tide

At the top of the beach at the upper limit of the high tides is the strand line often on sand or shingle. The upper limit of high tides on a rocky shore is normally referred to as the splash zone.

Down the shore from the strand line or splash zone is the Upper Shore. It is the area between the top of the high spring tides and the top of the high neap tides. It is exposed to the air for long periods of time and animal and plant life has adapted itself to this environment. The plants are able to withstand a drying out effect from both sun and wind. The animals will hide in crevices or bury themselves under seaweed, sand or stones. Some, like the Smooth Periwinkle, have a modified gill chamber which enables them to breathe in air as well as take in oxygen from the sea water. The salinity of the water in rock pools at this level often changes dramatically after torrential rain, as will the water temperature after a hot summer day. To survive in this habitat the plants or animals need to be tolerant of such extremes. As a result, the number of species in this zone is less than in the others.

Below the Upper Shore is the Middle Shore. This is the area between high water at neap tides and low water at neap tides. On an average beach in the Channel Islands, it is the largest of the three zones and is the area which is exposed and submerged twice in every twenty-four hours. Many of the animals are able to remain in pools or under wet seaweed or sand until the tide covers them again. Some, like the Limpet, will attach themselves to rocks, trapping moisture under the shell to provide enough oxygen for them until they are submerged again. The snail-like molluscs conceal themselves within their shell behind an operculum which acts like a trap door, thus retaining essential moisture.

At the bottom of the beach is the Lower Shore, i.e. the area between low water at neap tides and low water at spring tides. It is only exposed to the air for a few hours each month when the tide falls below the mean low water level. The majority of animal life is unable to survive any length of time exposed to the air and many of the red seaweeds found at this level are very delicate and would not tolerate the effect of wave action experienced higher up the shore.

Each zone on the shore has been taken separately, commencing with the splash zone at extreme high water and proceeding down the shore. The species shown can be found on almost all the beaches in the Channel Islands and wherever possible common names have been used as well as scientific names.

In each zone there are inevitably the rock pools. These can be very rewarding. Fishes, prawns, crabs and snail-like molluscs are the most obvious of the creatures to be found in this habitat. Then, of course, there are the sedentary animals like the anemones, sponges and hydroids to look for, as well as many seaweeds.

CODE OF CONDUCT

When you are pottering on the seashore please remember always to turn stones back to their original position as the plant life on the upper surface will not survive, primarily due to lack of light, and likewise the animal life on the underside will die quickly due to exposure if left turned over for even a small period of time.

STRAND LINE

Plate 1

The strand line is the area of flotsam and jetsam left by each high tide. It is nearly always rewarding to walk along any strand line to see what the tide has brought in. Often you will find seaweed or shells which have been washed up from quite deep water.

Egg cases often called Mermaid's Purse of Lesser spotted dogfish (*Scyliorhinus canicula*) **and of Skate** (*Raja sp.*)

1. **Lesser spotted dogfish**: The horny egg cases, probably of the Lesser Spotted Dog Fish, are approximately six cm in length, often still attached to pieces of seaweed by twisted tendrils coming from each corner. They are laid below low water mark, amongst seaweed, by the female fish and then torn away either after the embryo has hatched or by rough seas.

2. **Skate:** The egg case of the Skate is similar, but has four tapering corners instead of long twisted tendrils and is less elongated.

3. **Egg cases of Common Whelk** (*Buccinum undatum*)

   These are found washed up on the strandline. They are often the size of a tennis ball and made up of many inflated compartments which are almost weightless. Each egg-case houses about 100 eggs, of which only a few hatch. The remaining eggs become a source of food for the young snails until they are ready to crawl out into the open sea, where they have been laid, which is the normal habitat for the Common Whelk. Generally only the empty shell is found washed up on the strandline, as it is not a true inhabitant of the shore.

4. **Cuttlebone of common cuttlefish** (*Sepia officinalis*)

   This is the internal skeleton of a Cuttlefish. It is white, very light in weight and of porous structure. It acts as a buoyancy aid for the live Cuttlefish.

5. **Sea Slater** (*Ligia oceanica*)

They are found on the splash zone above high water mark. They often hide during the day under stones or in cracks and crevices in rocks or in the sea wall. Their colouring blends in with the background and they can reach up to 2.5cm in length. They do not survive if submerged in water. They feed at night, like the Sandhopper, on seaweeds or any debris that they can find. There are seven pairs of identical legs and two long antennae about two-thirds the length of the body.

6. **Sandhopper** (*Orchestia gammarella*)

There are several species of Sandhoppers and they are without doubt the animal of the strandline. They are abundant and can easily be found by turning over the seaweed. They immediately make their presence known by leaping or hopping about until they find shelter again or burrow into the sand. Careful searching will reveal their burrows. Adults are 1.6cm in length, do not like being exposed to the light and feed at night by scavenging on rotting seaweed and other decomposing matter. The body is laterally compressed, i.e. flattened sideways and the tail end is slightly curled under.

UPPER SHORE

Plate 2

As you start to walk down the majority of our rocky shores, the most dominant feature is the mass of brown seaweed (wracks). At first glance it appears to be one species, but on close investigation several kinds will be seen in very clearly marked zones, like bands across the shore. These seaweeds provide both shelter and food for many creatures, the most obvious being the snail-like periwinkles.

UPPER SHORE POOLS

The salinity of these pools varies. Torrential rain, when the tide is down, will dilute the water, while the salinity will become more concentrated through evaporation during very hot weather. Therefore, the variety of life on the upper shore pools will be less than those on the middle and lower shore, because few creatures can tolerate these rapidly changing conditions.

1. **Small Periwinkle** (*Littorina neritoides*)

    Just above high water mark, in the splash zone, the Small Periwinkle can often be found hiding in crevices of the rocks, especially on shores that are exposed to rough seas. It is very small, 0.5cm high, blue-black in colour, and has a smooth shell with the appearance of a bloom similar to that which can be seen on grapes. It feeds by browsing on minute lichens.

2. **Rough Periwinkle** (*Littorina 'saxatilis' aggregate*)

    The Rough Periwinkle is up to 0.8cm high with a thick shell, rough to the touch caused by ridges and grooves. The colour is variable, ranging from white to dark orange, brown and some with banded stripes. They are very common and can be found browsing over Channelled Wrack and on rocks, stones and pools. Some species of Rough Periwinkle are ovo-viviporous, that is, the fertilised egg-cases remain within the body cavity of the female during the brooding period, which enables the fully formed young to hatch out onto the correct zone. The Rough Periwinkle is thought by some to be a source of food for crabs, as well as some shore birds such as oystercatchers and gulls.

3. ***Enteromorpha* species**

    Most of the grass-like seaweeds found on the upper shore belong to the genus *Enteromorpha* and are difficult to separate into specific species without microscopic study. *Enteromorpha sp.* are very tolerant of low salinity and are often found where freshwater land drains are situated. They are annual and many of the developing spores, which settle on rocky surfaces, are quickly browsed upon by limpets and other molluscs. They grow very rapidly in spring and can form a green covering on sand in early summer.

4.   **Sea Lettuce** (*Ulva lactuca*)

Named Sea Lettuce because of its broad lettuce-like green fronds. It is also found in brackish water and thrives in slightly polluted water. It can be eaten raw, as part of a salad or boiled like spinach. Make sure you collect any to eat from clean water!

5.   **Channelled Wrack** (*Pelvetia canaliculata*)

This is the first established brown seaweed to be found as you start to wander down the shore. It may appear soft and glistening with a golden hue if the tide has just fallen, or it may be hard, dry and brittle if it has been left exposed to both sun and wind for some time. A close look at the stipe (or stalk) of the seaweed will show that it is grooved or channelled on one side only. This side generally lies against the rock and retains enough moisture to keep the fronds from dehydrating completely. During the summer the tips of the plant become swollen and yellow in colour. These are the reproductive receptacles. The tufts can be very dense and grow up to 15cm in length. Channelled Wrack will not survive if continually submerged in water. Therefore, because of its position on the shore, it is not a suitable habitat for many creatures, but it is a source of food for the Sea Slater (plate 1) and for the Rough Periwinkle.

6.   **Spiral Wrack** (*Fucus spiralis*)

It has tough, brown, leathery fronds, and no air bladders, but is slightly twisted towards the tips, which may at times appear swollen and resemble sultanas when the fruiting receptacles become mature. This is found just a little further down the shore from the Channelled Wrack.

MIDDLE SHORE
Plate 3

1. **Toothed or Thick Topshell** (*Monodonta lineata*)

    As you move down the shore you will come across this Topshell which can be up to 2.5 cm in length. Inside the shell and around the opening is a layer of mother-of-pearl. A conspicuous white tooth, or dent, can be seen on the edge of the shell opening. The remainder of the shell is grey-green-purple in a zig-zag pattern. The tip, or apex, of the shell may show a pearly yellow colour in older, worn specimens. These molluscs have to withstand wave action twice every day and are often found sheltering in numbers on the leeward side of rocks. They are often thought incorrectly to be the Common Edible Winkle, which is in fact uncommon in the Channel Islands.

2. **Bladder Wrack** (*Fuscus vesiculosus*)

    This seaweed covers the largest area in the middle part of the shore and attaches itself to rocks, piers and in fact, to anything that is solid. Like all the wracks, it is brown, tough and leathery. It has conspicuous air-bladders, generally in pairs, all along the fronds. These air-bladders act as a buoyancy aid for the plant to raise the fronds towards the light as the tide rises. The swollen yellower tips which occur in early summer are signs of maturing reproductive receptacles. These are not to be confused with the air-bladders. Bladder Wrack is a source of food and shelter for numerous other forms of life.

3. **Flat Periwinkle** (*Littorina littoralis*)

    These are found in large numbers hiding or browsing on bladder wrack. The shell is smooth and the colour varies from bright orange to yellow, green and brown. Some may even have banded markings. The colour, size and shape helps to keep the animal obscured from predators as they resemble the air-bladders and the fruiting bodies of seaweeds. The Flat Periwinkle lays egg masses on the seaweed fronds. These look like blobs of clear jelly, about the size of a small fingernail. During the summer months, if you look very carefully you should be able to find some. Within the jelly there are hundreds of minute eggs which develop into young snails and will, within a month, eat their way out and into the seaweed to start their own cycle of life.

4. **Spirorbis borealis**

This is a worm which lives in a hard limy tube, formed by itself. From this, when covered by the tide, it will extend a crown of feathery tentacles which filters particles of food and extracts oxygen from the water for breathing. At the tip of one tentacle there is a small club-shaped operculum (a hard structure) which acts as a door to the entrance of the tube and traps enough moisture to keep the worm from dehydrating when exposed to air. The tube is coiled in a clockwise direction. Should you find one that is coiled in an anti-clockwise direction, it is most likely to be another variety *Spirorbis spirillum*. These worms retain their fertilised eggs within the cavity of the limy tube. The young hatch out directly onto the fronds of the seaweed and immediately attach themselves to the surface and start building their own tubes.

5. **Knotted Wrack** (*Ascophyllum nodosum*)

This seaweed is characteristic of sheltered shores though some tufts of this species can be found on almost all the beaches. You will notice that on a very sheltered shore it will almost completely take over the Bladder Wrack zone. Consisting of a long flat stipe it can grow up to 150cm in length and tufts as old as 12 years have been recorded. The aging of this plant is done by counting the very conspicuous oval airbladders, which are well spaced apart along the stipe. One bladder is produced each year, once the plant is two years old. The side branches, which are much thinner, produce the reproductive bodies and like the other wracks resemble sultanas on maturity.

6. **Polysiphonia lanosa**

This is a short tufted red seaweed which can often be found growing on Knotted Wrack. If you look at it through a hand lens you will see that there are numerous fine, almost hair-like branches growing from a holdfast. Holdfasts are the root-like structures which anchor the seaweed to rocks, piers, other seaweeds etc. They are able to grip into rock crevices, gaining a firm enough hold to prevent dislodgement by the pounding action of the waves.

Unlike terrestrial plants, seaweeds do not need a root system to absorb the required nutrients for growth, for they are able to absorb everything by infusion. A plant such as this, which only attaches itself to another but does not take nourishment from it, is called an epiphyte.

H YDROIDS (SOMETIMES REFERRED TO AS S EA F IRS)

Still looking amongst the wracks at mid-tide level, especially amongst the Knotted Wrack, you will find Hydroids growing on these plants. They are not plants but are in fact sedentary (attached) colonial coelenterates, which is the name given to this group of animal life and includes the jelly fish and anemones. They look like fine strands of straw about 3cm high and are most likely to be either *Obelia geniculata* or *Dynamena pumila*.

7.   **Obelia geniculata**. The stems are irregularly branched and zig-zagged. With the aid of a hand lens you should be able to see at each joint a ringed stalk supporting an urn-shaped opening from which emerges a ring of tentacles similar to that of an anemone. These are used for trapping particles of food from the water.

8.   **Dynamena pumila.** This is a similar species to the above, except that the stem is straight and the openings are not on stalks and are arranged in regular opposite pairs.

MIDDLE SHORE
Plate 4

1.   **Purple Topshell** (*Gibbula umbilicalis*)

This is a rather flattened, purple zig-zag striped snail, abundant on all rocky areas, especially where seaweed is common. One very obvious identification characteristic is the small hole (umbilicus) which can be found on the underside of the shell near the opening. Like all other snail-like molluscs on the shore, the Purple Topshell closes itself inside the shell by means of a horny disc (operculum) to prevent it drying out when exposed at low tide. Otherwise it would die from dehydration.

2. **Common Limpet** (*Patella vulgata*)

Limpets can be easily found on all rocky shores, often in great numbers. They have conical shells and when exposed, adhere to the rocks to such an extent they are difficult to dislodge without damaging them. All Limpets are herbivores and generally feed when covered by the tide, when they 'graze' over the rocks with their radula, which is a long rasp-like tongue, scraping minute growths of seaweed, often too small to see with the naked eye. Limpets will 'home' back to the same spot after each feeding session. Their shells are moulded to the exact shape of the rock. This enables them to trap a drop of water within the shell before the tide falls, which will provide enough moisture to prevent the animals from dehydrating.

3. **Acorn Barnacles** (*Semibalanus balanoides*)

These are abundant on rocky exposed shores. In some instances boulders may have up to a 90% cover of barnacles. They are sessile, which means they cannot move. Adults are up to 1.5cm diameter, resembling tiny volcanoes, greyish in colour. Young specimens are much whiter. The hard outer casing, the exoskeleton, is made up of six calcified plates, which can be seen through a hand lens. The centre or apex is of a diamond shape from which, when submerged by the sea, feathery appendages called cirri emerge and filter small particles of food from the water. This central opening is covered by the upper plates (operculum). Another common barnacle, found slightly higher on the shore, is *Chthamalus montagui*, which is similar to the above except that the centre opening is kite shaped. It is found at a slightly higher level and is less numerous.

4. **Dog Whelk** (*Nucella lapillus*)

Dog whelks are carnivorous and can often be found feeding on Acorn Barnacles. They are white when young but become grey as they mature. A siphonal groove can be found in the shell aperture (opening). This groove allows the whelk to extend a siphon in order to draw in a clean supply of water, which flows over the gills to provide oxygen, essential for respiration. Females can often be found lower down on the shore laying their eggs.

5.   Egg-cases of Dog Whelk

Lower down on the shore you can often find under boulders or overhanging rocks clusters of yellow vase-shaped capsules about 5mm high. These are the egg cases of the Dog Whelk. Several females will often congregate in the same area, laying approximately 15 egg-cases, each containing up to 100 minute eggs, of which only 7-10 will be fertile. The newly hatched Dog Whelk will then eat the remaining eggs and after about 16 weeks emerge from the vase-shaped capsule and start its life on the open shore.

6.   Bread-crumb Sponge (*Halichondria panicea*)

Some forms of marine life are unable to tolerate exposure for any length of time, so need to be protected from dehydration by overhanging rocks or by being covered by seaweed. The Breadcrumb Sponge, varying in colour from yellow-orange-green, is an example, as it is often found under seaweeds from mid shore to low water mark. Sponges are very simple animals, made up of living cells held together by minute spicules, which are tiny skeletal rods. Water is absorbed through pores from all over the surface and is moved through channels by minute beating hairs called flagellae so that food and oxygen is extracted and the water then passes out through the oscula, which are openings resembling volcanic cones. Bread-crumb Sponge is one of the few sponges which can be easily recognised. Most sponges found on the shore need to be identified with the aid of a microscope.

7.   Sea Belt or Sugar Kelp (*Laminaria saccharina*)

Often found in places where a permanent stream seems to flow, this weed can be attached to quite small stones by a claw-like holdfast. Seaweeds do not have roots like land plants. Their nutrients are absorbed through pores all over the plant, so the root-like structure is used only for anchorage. Sea Belt has a wavy, almost frilled appearance, looking very much like a crocodile skin. If allowed to dry in the sun, a fine white sweet-tasting substance called mannitol appears on the surface. This seaweed is often used as part of a supplement for animal fodder. It can grow up to two metres in length.

8.   **Toothed or Serrated Wrack** (*Fucus serratus*)

This is the last of the wracks to be found as we move down the beach. It is easily identified by the serrated edge of the flat fronds, absence of bladders and is slightly more orange in colour than the other wracks higher up on the shore. The tips of the fronds are forked and in the autumn swell up into fruiting bodies, resembling sultanas, which when mature, discharge a thick orange-yellow mucus into the sea.

LOWER SHORE
Plate 5

The area between low-water neaps and low-water springs is by far the richest area in both quantity and variety. The animals and plants living in this zone are less tolerant of extreme changes of water and air temperatures and in some ways 'softer' - unable to withstand continuous wave action. This section of the shore is only exposed for a very short time on a few days each month. The red seaweeds dominate the top part of this zone, with the large brown leathery Oar weeds at extreme low water and beyond. The red seaweeds are numerous and often impossible to identify without microscopic study. However, there are one or two which are easily recognised.

CARRAGHEEN (SOMETIMES CALLED IRISH MOSS)

1.   *Chondrus crispus*

This is dark red, often in pools and up to 6cm in height. It is found in tufts on rocks and boulders, often with a blue or violet iridescence in strong sunlight. The fronds are flattened, fairly tough, branching in pairs or forked (dichotomus). This seaweed was collected by islanders during World War Two and used as a setting agent for milk jellies. This was done by washing the seaweed several times, then leaving it to bleach in the sun until it became a creamy white colour and quite dry and crisp. It was then crushed or minced into fine powder. Approximately 1 oz of powdered Carragheen to l pt of milk was used. It was boiled for about 10 minutes, and the liquid was then strained through fine muslin and allowed to set.

2.   *Gigartina stellata*

Also known as Carragheen, this is similar to *Chondrus crispus* though it can grow up to 20cm long. The flattened fronds become in-rolled to form a channel at the base, which distinguishes it from the above. Older fronds may be covered with numerous small wart-like lumps, which are the fruiting bodies.

3.   Dulse (*Palmaria palmata*)

This is abundant at low water, looking a little like red lettuce leaves or spinach. Small leaflets grow from the edges of the fronds, which are very tender. If you are able to spread out a frond, it will look a little like the palm of a hand - hence the name *palmata*..

4.   Pepper Dulse (*Laurencia pinnatifida*)

This is a small red seaweed which varies in colour considerably from olive green in exposed places to a dull dark red in shady sheltered zones. It sometimes covers large areas of rock and can grow up to 10cm in length. The frond is strong, flat and divided alternately. The branchlets grow progressively shorter towards the tip.

5.   *Lomentaria articulata*

Another common red seaweed found near low water. Pink to crimson in colour, it grows up to 20cm in length. The branches are constricted into small, shiny articulated sections resembling a string of sausages or beads.

ANEMONES

Anemones are fairly primitive forms of animal life. They have one central opening in the centre of the tentacles into which food and oxygen are taken and from which all waste and sexual products are passed. There are several anemones to be found by careful searching. The two obvious ones are:

6. **Beadlet Anemone** (*Actinia equina*)

The anemone's numerous tentacles are able to capture food by stunning their prey with minute stinging cells (invisible to the naked eye) and then transferring the food to the mouth which is situated in the centre of the tentacles. These stinging cells are quite harmless to humans. If you touch the tentacles you will be aware of a slight suction, almost a sticky feeling. The Beadlet Anemone will withdraw its tentacles right inside the column of its body when exposed or disturbed and it will then look like a small blob of red jelly. This anemone will incubate fertilised eggs within the body cavity and the live young are ejected from the central opening. It is the commonest of all our anemones and can be found in shady places and in pools, especially on exposed coasts, where some may be green or brown in colour. Occasionally some with yellowish speckles all over the column may be found. They are the **Strawberry Anemones.**

7. **Snakeslocks Anemone** (*Anemonia sulcata*)

It is not as abundant as the Beadlet, but easily recognised by its larger size and longer tentacles, which can be grey-brown or green with purple tips. The green colour is, in fact, an algae, which lives symbiotically (a close relationship between animal and plant which benefits both) within the tissue of the tentacles. This anemone cannot withdraw its tentacles, so if left exposed it appears a floppy mess. Generally it will be found in water, fairly low down on the shore where there is good sunlight.

8. **Cushion Starfish** (*Asterina gibbosa*)

The place to find this attractive starfish is under rocks and boulders at low water. It has a star-shaped body, rough to the touch, usually green or brown in colour on the upper parts and yellow-orange underneath. This is where the mouth is situated in a central disc. The rest of the underparts have many minute tube feet which enable the starfish to climb over the rocks and to move in any direction.

9. **Topshell** (*Gibbula pennanti*)

This is found on the lower shore, and is similar to the Purple Topshell which lives higher up on the shore. *Gibbula pennanti* however, has no umbilicus (a small hole in the centre of the shell, on the underside). The shell pattern and colour is generally more pronounced but still in a zig-zag design. This is a Channel Islands species which is not found on the English side of the Channel. Care should be taken not to confuse this species with Toothed Topshell.

10. **Grey Topshell** (*Gibbula cineraria*)

This is another snail-like mollusc, greyer, with a fine geometric pattern, generally found at extreme low-water. All the top-shells have a mother-of-pearl lining to the inside of the shell and all have a horny operculum (trapdoor) to seal the opening of the shell when exposed to the air by the falling tide.

11. **Painted Topshell** (*Calliostoma zizyphinum*)

This is by far the most striking of all the coiled shells to be found. Live specimens are only found on rocks at extreme low water. It is conical shaped, up to 2.5cm high with bright colour patterns of yellow-pink, with brown and red markings. It is very colourful, easily recognised, and common in a very small zone only.

12. **Bootlace Weed** (*Chorda filum*)

This looks like a single cord, round and tapering to a point - never with branches. It is often found washed up on the shore, although it only grows at the lowest levels. It can grow up to 8 metres.

13. **The Ormer** (*Haliotis tuberculata*)

No book on the shore life of the Channel Islands can pass without some mention of the Ormer.

Regrettably this once abundant mollusc is now a rare find. The ear-shaped shells with their lovely mother-of-pearl lining are now almost collectors' items, although there are still some to be found after diligent searching at extremely low tides. Some fishermen are experimenting in farming these local delicacies and the Guernsey States Sea Fisheries Committee is running trials with the aim of replenishing natural stocks.

Since the 1870s the number of ormers around Guernsey has been noticeably decreasing and it was at that time that the first regulations and restrictions on the collection and sale of ormers were introduced.

Many suggestions for the decline of the ormer around our shores have been voiced. They include an increase of the ormer gatherers, the introduction of motor boats (making Herm and other offshore rocks accessible), the constant turning over of stones at low water mark destroying the ormer's natural food supply, the disregard in many instances of the minimum size rule (collecting below 8cms) and the quantities collected in more recent years by divers. Collection by divers has now been banned.

At the present time the collecting of ormers is limited in the Bailiwick of Guernsey to the days of the full or new moon and three days thereafter, between the 1st January and 30th April inclusive. It is an offence to take ormers at any other time.

In Jersey similar restrictions apply, although the season for gathering ormers is from September to April inclusive. The collecting of ormers for commercial use is discouraged.

The conservation of the ormer can be encouraged by always replacing boulders and stones in their original position.

It must be pointed out that the Channel Islands are at the most northerly tip of the ormer range, which extends as far south as Guinea, just north of the equator. At the centre of its range, in the region of the Azores and Mediterranean, temperatures are always correct for successful breeding, whereas this can be affected if water temperatures are too cold here in the north of its range or too hot in the south. However it is quite normal, even in these areas, for numbers to fluctuate for reasons not yet known.

LOWER SHORE SEAWEEDS
Plate 6

1.   **Thongweed** (*Himanthalia elongata*)

This is very common in Guernsey and Alderney, especially on steep sides of boulders at low water. It is olive brown in colour, and can reach up to three metres in length. It consists of long narrow, flat, leathery, strap-like fronds, growing from a disc which resembles a shiny brown mushroom and looks at first like small antlers or horns. Rare in Jersey.

OAR WEEDS

There are four Oar Weeds which look very similar at first glance, but on closer investigation can be easily separated, often washed up on to the strandline. These large brown seaweeds are commonly referred to as kelps.

2.   *Laminaria digitata*

This is probably the most common. It has long brown leathery wide fronds, divided into fingers with a smooth supple stipe (stalk) and a claw-like holdfast by which it attaches itself to the rocks. When exposed by the tide, the Oar Weeds look like weeping branches and can grow up to three metres in length, but those found growing on the shore are generally about one metre in length.

3.   *Laminaria hyperborea*

This is very similar to *Laminaria digitata* but generally found at a level below low water, though it is frequently washed up on to the shore. The main characteristic difference is the stipe which is ridged and rough and in mature specimens will often have other algae or animal life living on it.

Laminaria ochroleuca (not illustrated)

This is similar to *Laminaria hyperborea* but the frond is much yellower and the stipe stiff but smooth.

4.   Furbelows (*Saccorhiza polyschides*)

This plant, like *Laminaria hyperborea* generally grows at sub-littoral levels (below low water) and is easily recognised by the large bulbous holdfast, which is hollow, knobbly and perforated. The stipe is flattened and spirally twisted at the base with wavy frills. It can grow to an enormous size.

5.   Dabberlocks (*Alaria esculenta*)

This has a long yellow-brown leafy frond and is found at low water on exposed shores. It is very common in Alderney, but only occasionally washed up on the shore in the other islands. It has a distinct mid-rib through the centre of the frond and small fruiting bodies at the base of the stipe.

ROCK POOLS
Plate 7

These are mostly found in the middle shore zone and are perhaps the most rewarding areas to search, with a rich and varied flora and fauna.

1.   Coral Weed (*Corallina officinalis*)

This is found around the edges of most pools. It is very brittle, pink, encrusted with lime, and sometimes bleached white when exposed. It is very common.

2. **Lithophyllum sp. and Lithothamnion sp.**

These are encrusting seaweeds which are very difficult to separate, even with a hand lens. They look almost like hard dried purple paint splodges covering the rocks in or around pools. However they are very common and can be generally found in shady places. Some are very knobbly.

3. **Codium sp.**

This is dark green, up to 45cm in length, with many branches. It has a soft, spongelike texture and feels like velvet to touch. The tips of the fronds look like small antlers. In spring and summer a small green sea slug **4. Elysia viridis** can often be found on Codium. This sea slug is about 3cm length, beautifully marked with pale spots around the margin and it both feeds and lays eggs on the fronds of Codium.

5. **Rainbow Bladderweed** (*Cystoseira tamariscifolia*)

This a bushy golden brown seaweed with iridescent green-blue colour when under water and small airbladders over the fronds. It is very common in deep pools.

6. **Japweed** (*Sargassum muticum*)

This seaweed has only established itself in the Channel Islands since 1981. It is now becoming a common seaweed on our coasts. It is an annual which grows very rapidly from May to July to a length of 3 metres or more. It has many side branches along the stipe with numerous bladders. It is brown and young plants can be confused with the Rainbow Bladderweed above. Japweed is abundant around the Ecréhous, S.E. of Jersey and occurs widely around the coast of all the Channel Islands where there is standing water. It is less common in Alderney.

PRAWNS AND SHRIMPS

There are several species of prawns to be found in almost all pools during the summer months. Sometimes they can be difficult to see against a background of green seaweed, as they are quite transparent (only turning pink when cooked). When disturbed, they will dart backwards through the water. There are three things to note to help you to distinguish a prawn from a shrimp:

i.   Shrimps are found on sandy shores, generally in sandy pools or at the edge of the tide, whereas prawns are always in rock pools amongst seaweed.

ii.   Shrimps are flattened in shape from top to bottom. Prawns are flattened from side to side.

iii. Prawns have a long serrated rostrum, which is like a sword, protruding from the head-part of the outer skeleton. This rostrum is absent in shrimps.

The most common one of each of the above are

7.   **the Common Shrimp** (*Crangon vulgaris*) and

8.   **the Common Prawn** (*Leander serratus*).

FISH

There are numerous small fish to be found in the rock pools and water-filled gullies, especially at low water, and a name given by local people to cover all of them is the **Cabot**. There are however, three which are probably the most common:

9.   **Common Blenny** (*Blennius pholis*)

This is a rather thick-bodied fish with a dorsal fin running along its length (on its back) and an anal fin, half as long (on its underside). It has large eyes and is variable in colour from dark green to yellow, with banded or blotched markings.

10. **Goby** (*Gobius sp.*)

The Goby is very common in rock pools. It has what appears to be two dorsal fins, the one nearest the head being very spiny. Its colour is variable and it is more tapered than the Blenny.

11. **Butterfish** (*Pholis gunnellus*)

This little fish is found at low water under stones and seaweed. It has a very slippery skin, hence the name Butterfish. Running along the whole length of the body just below the fin is a row of very distinctive black spots, circled in white, which stand out quite clearly on the dark body. These fish can reach up to 20cm in length.

SANDY SHORE AND CRABS
Plate 8

Crabs belong to a group of animals called Crustacea, which have a hard exoskeleton (a skeleton on the outside of the body). The hard shell-like covering of the body is called the carapace. This provides protection for the crab, like a coat of armour. Crabs have a pair of pincers or claws called chelae and four pairs of walking legs, each pair slightly different.

In order to grow, crabs have to moult and shed their hard shells. Before this can happen a new exoskeleton is formed beneath the old one, only it is soft and wrinkled. Then the crab will hide under seaweed or in a crevice, away from its predators. After taking in a large amount of water and loosening its new skin away from the old, splits eventually occur along the edges of the carapace which are known as a pre-formed line of weakness. The crab is then able to squeeze itself out backwards through these splits. This takes up to 2-3 hours. At this point the crab is very vulnerable as the new shell is soft, easily damaged and it is easy prey. Gradually the soft new exoskeleton stretches out and is no longer wrinkled and the crab will expand to its new size. After several days it will harden, as it becomes impregnated with calcium salts from the sea and will stay like this until it moults again.

LUGWORM (ARENICOLA MARINA)

This is a segmented worm, settling at first on the top of the shore whilst still small, then moving down the shore as it grows bigger.

1. **Lugworm Cast**

One of the first signs of life that you find on a sandy shore is the worm cast made by the lugworm which lives in a U-shaped burrow below the surface of the sand. The worm produces a mucus which lines and strengthens the burrow. For up to eight hours a day the lugworm will feed by swallowing sand from one end of its burrow and extracting food particles from it, usually detritus which is rotting seaweed. If you look carefully you may see a depression in the sand which marks the head end of the burrow. At intervals of six or seven minutes the lugworm will shuffle backwards and deposit the waste sand at the tail end of the burrow, thus forming the familiar coiled sandy cast.

2. **Sandmason Worm Tube** (*Lanice conchilega*)

This is found below midshore in tubes made of particles of sand and shell. Each tube, up to 30cm in length, is uniquely formed by the worm, with only about 2-3cm exposed above the surface of the sand. The end appears to be frayed with delicate strands of sand grains. When the tide covers the tube the worm will extend delicate tentacles which collect particles of food from the flow of water. The actual worm is only 2-3cm long.

BIVALVES

Bivalve molluscs have two shells which are hinged together. Some, like mussels, attach themselves to rocks, piers etc. Others, like cockles, are able to bury themselves in sand. They all draw in a current of water which passes over the gills to supply oxygen and over the mouth where minute particles of food are extracted from the water. Bivalve molluscs have no distinct head or tail end. Empty shells are often found on the shore, usually only one half, as they get torn apart by the waves. If you look carefully you will see small, almost circular depressions on the inside of the shell. These are where the animal was once attached and are called muscle scars. Along the hinge line you will see varying arrangements of teeth. Both these and the muscle scars are important factors in identification of empty shells. The following are the four most common bivalves to be found:

3. **Edible Cockle** (*Cerastoderma edule*)

Edible cockles are not found on all the sandy beaches. In Guernsey they are mostly found on the north-west coast, in Jersey mostly on the east and south coasts and in Alderney only occasionally. Over-collecting, from what were natural cockle beds, has reduced the numbers considerably. Attractive ribbed shells, with finer cross ridges, make them easily identifiable. They bury themselves just below the surface of the sand by digging with a white muscular foot. They then protrude two siphons, one to draw in fresh water from which oxygen is extracted and another through which the excess water and waste products are passed out.

4. **Razor Shells** (*Ensis sp.*)

The Razor Shell, which is long and narrow lives at the low water mark, deeply buried in the sand. It has two shells hinged together on one side, the other edge being almost razor sharp, enabling it to cut down through the sand very rapidly to flee from danger as its foot pulls it down to a depth of up to 50cms or more. Like the Edible Cockle it will, when near the surface of the sand, protrude two siphons to draw in water from which food and oxygen will be extracted, before it passes it out through the other siphon together with any waste products.

5. **Edible Mussels** (*Mytilus edulis*)

Mussels are not common throughout the C. I. but can be found in isolation in rock crevices. Empty shells can be found in large numbers near areas where they are farmed. They are easily recognised by their blue-black shells, the inside lined with a bluish pearl. Mussels attach themselves to rocks, piers or any solid material by several byssal threads which are formed by a fluid produced by the mussel and harden in the sea-water to form an anchor. In Guernsey, mussels are found most commonly on the south and west coasts. In Jersey and in Alderney they are only occasionally found.

Crabs moult many times during their lifetime, which can be up to three or four years. The males and females can be identified by the tail flap which is tucked underneath the body, being broad and rounded in the female and pointed in the male. When the female is carrying her eggs she is said to be in 'berry'.

6. **Common Shore Crab** (*Carcinus meanus*)

    This is the commonest crab and can be found over a wide area of shore, hiding under stones and seaweeds. Generally dark green with paler underparts, it can also be quite a bright orange-brown colour. When disturbed it will quickly crawl away sideways. The Common Shore Crab has three blunt teeth on the shell between the eyes and five quite sharp ones on either side. To pick up a crab without being nipped, grasp it firmly with thumb and first finger where the pincers join the shell.

7. **Edible Crab** (*Cancer pagurus*)

    Locally known as a Chancre (pronounced 'shanker'), the adults live in deep water but the young ones are found on our lower shores. This crab takes five years to reach maturity. It is easily recognised by its pink-brown shell which looks a little like a pie crust and is generally oval in shape, but very small ones are almost round. It is not as aggressive as the common shore crab.

8. **Velvet Swimming Crab** (*Macropipus (portunus) puber*)

    This is the most colourful and the fiercest of our shore crabs. The shell is a brownish-red with bright blue lines on the legs and joints and is covered with soft greyish hairs which feel like velvet to the touch. The last pair of legs are flattened to form paddles which help them to swim. Found on the lower parts of the shore.

9. **Hairy Crab** (*Pilumnus hirtellus*)

    This crab is only 2cm in length, with a red-brown shell covered in hairs. Its claws are rough to touch, one being larger than the other and a lighter colour than the shell. It is only found at low water, usually among the holdfasts of the larger Oar Weeds.

GLOSSARY

Anal fin	the fin on a fish's underside
Aperture	shell opening
Apex	the tip of a shell
Berry, in	said of a female crab carrying her eggs
Byssal threads	fluid threads produced and hardened in sea-water to form an anchor
Carapace	hard shell-like covering of a crab
Chelae	pincers or claws
Cirri	feathery appendages
Coelenterates	a group of species which includes hydroids, anemones and jelly fish
Dichotomus	forked or branched in pairs
Dorsal fin	the fin on a fish's back
Epiphyte	a plant which attaches itself to another but takes no nourishment from it
Exoskeleton	the hard outer casing
Flagellae	beating hairs
Gill	feather-like structure for taking in oxygen in fish and other marine species
Holdfasts	root-like structures which anchor seaweed to rocks etc
Hydroids	sedentary colonial coelenterates
Mannitol	a fine white sweet tasting substance
Operculum	a trapdoor / a horny disc / upper plates / a hard structure
Oscula	openings resembling volcanic cones
Radula	the long rasp-like tongue of limpets
Rostrum	a structure protruding from the head-part of the outer skeleton
Sedentary	attached to a base such as rock etc
Sessile	unable to move
Siphon	tube for drawing in water for oxygen and food and for ejecting waste
Spicules	tiny skeletal rods
Splash zone	the area just above high water mark
Stipe	stalk
Strand line	the area of flotsam and jetsam left by each high tide
Sub-littoral	below low water
Umbilicus	small hole near the opening of the shell

INDEX

Latin names are used where there is no English equivalent.

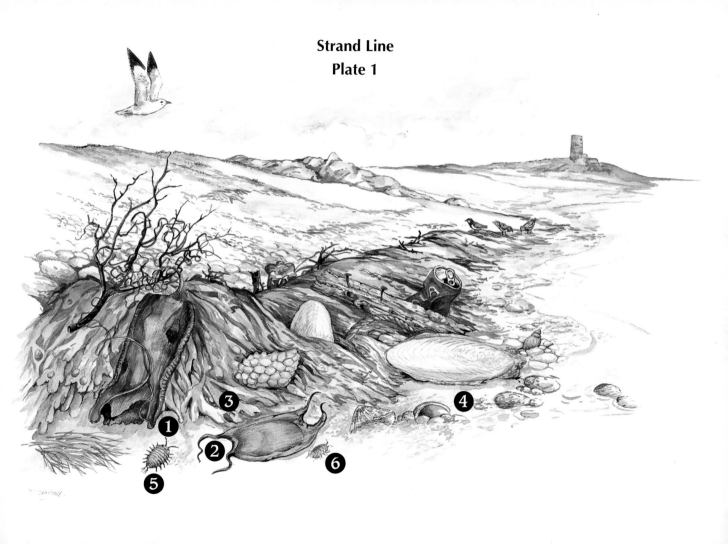

Strand Line

Plate 1

Upper Shore
Plate 2

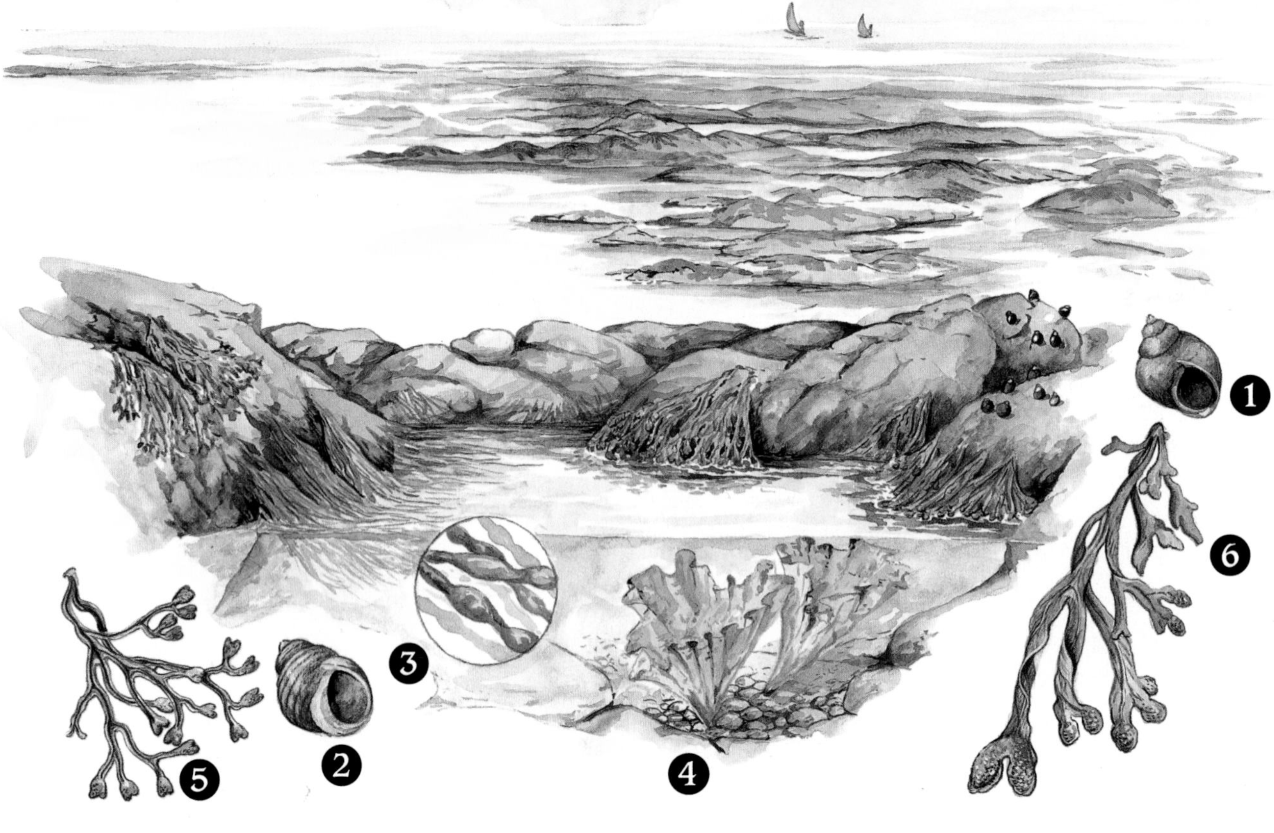

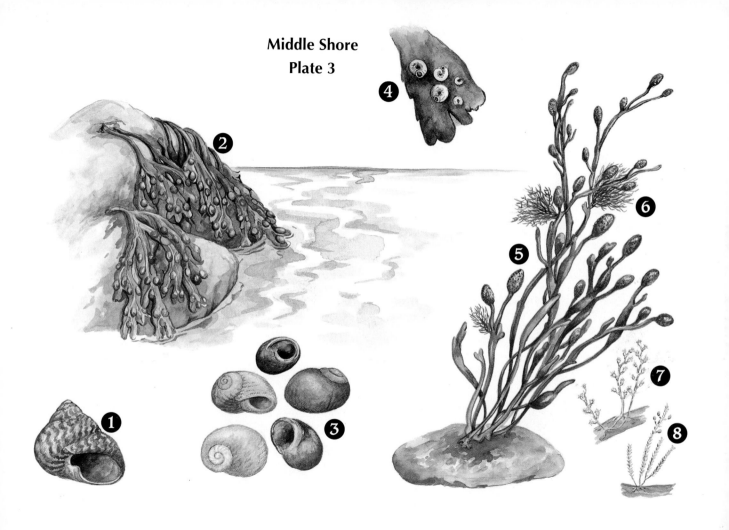

Middle Shore
Plate 3

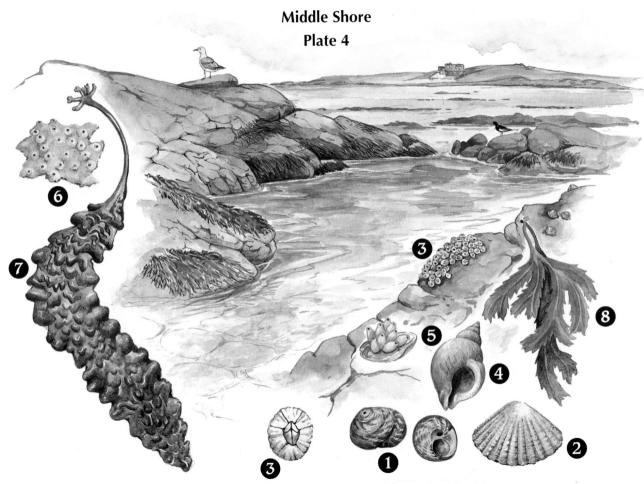

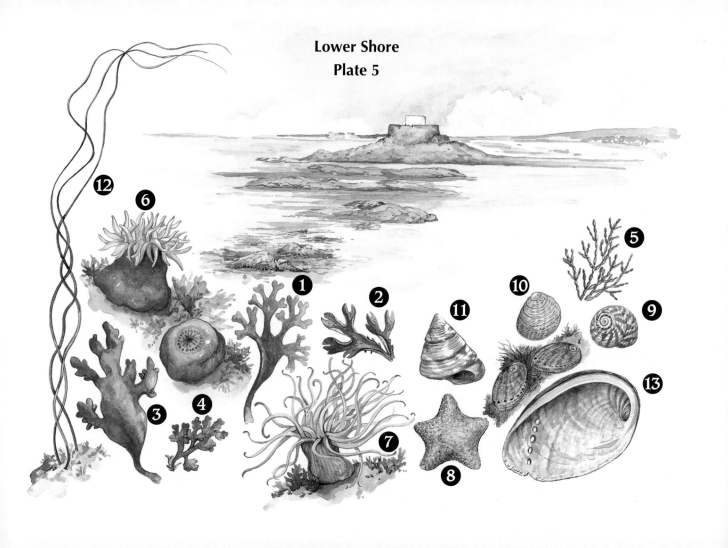

Lower Shore
Plate 5

Lower Shore Seaweeds
Plate 6

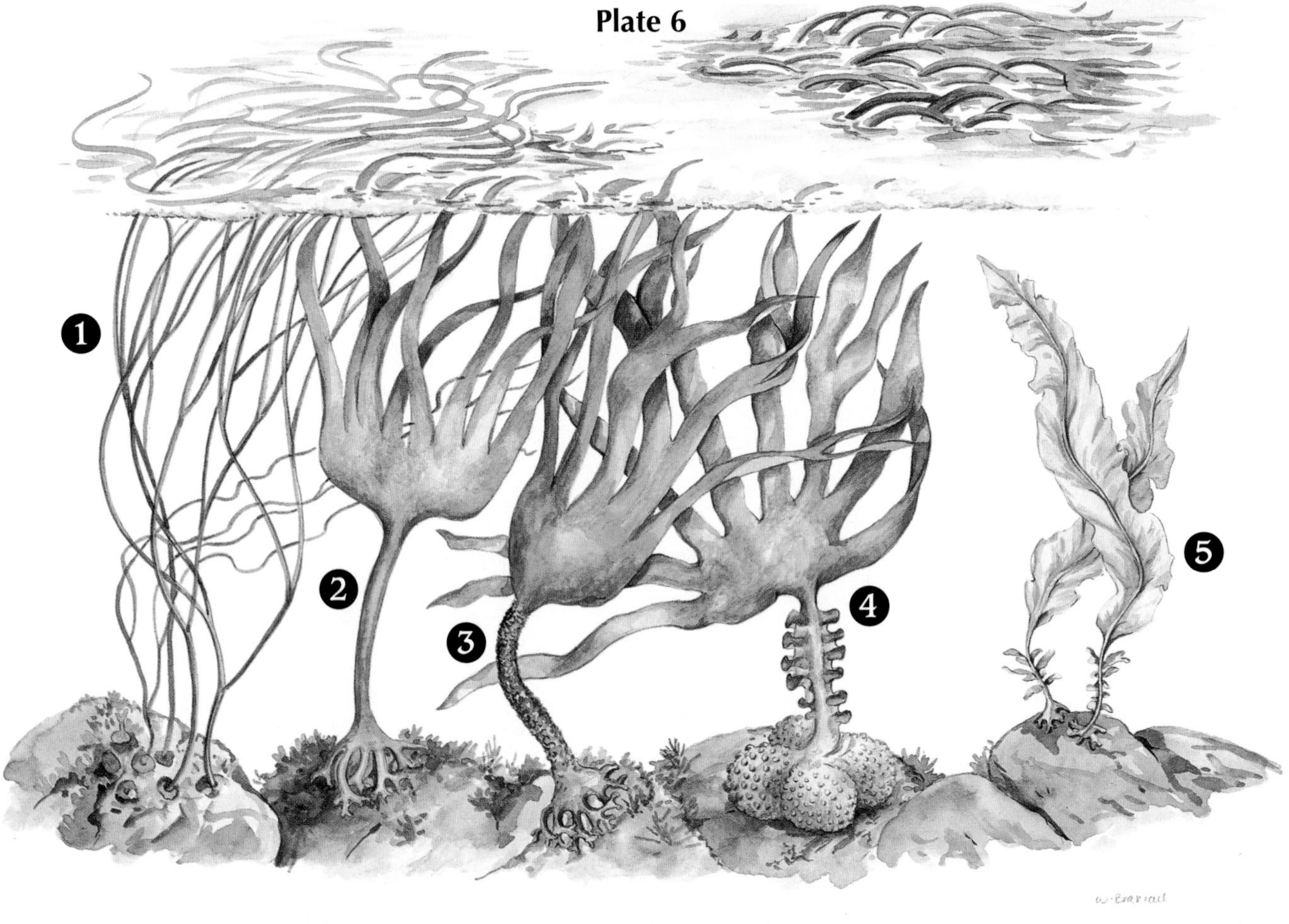

Rock Pools

Plate 7

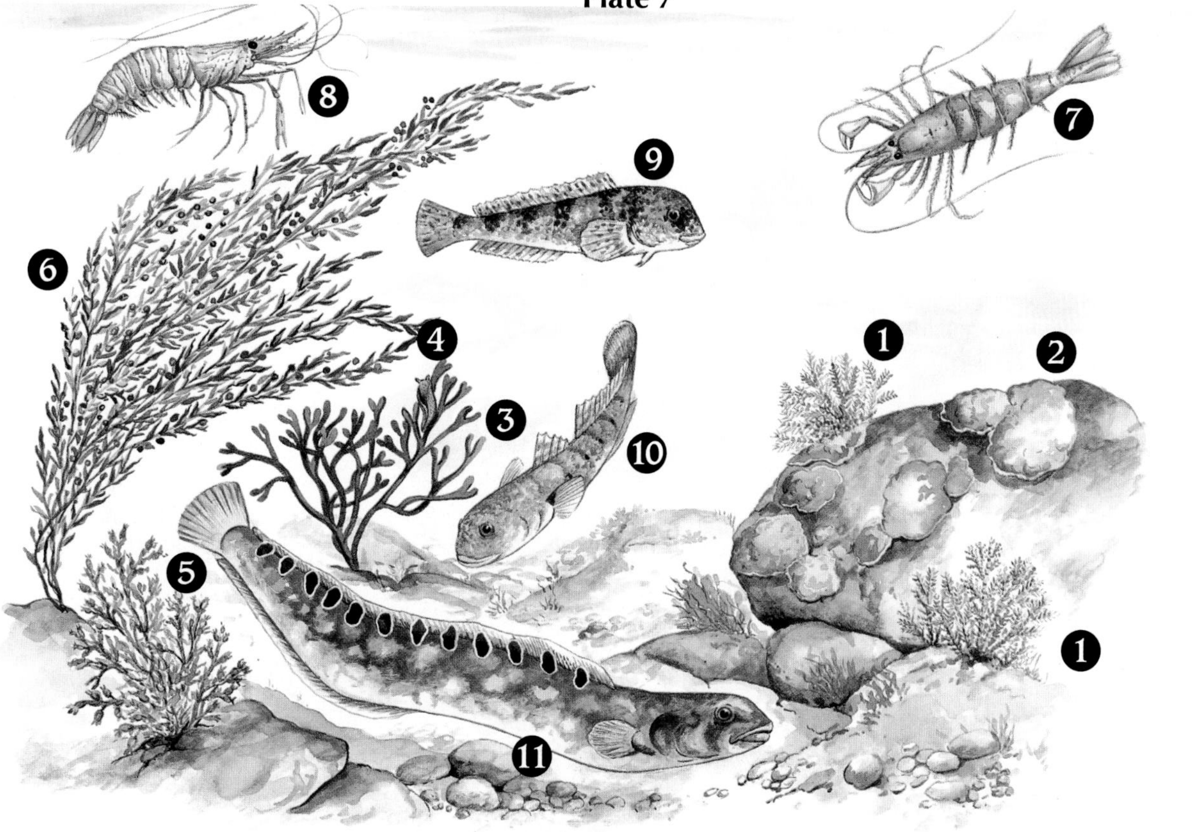

Sandy Shore and Crabs
Plate 8

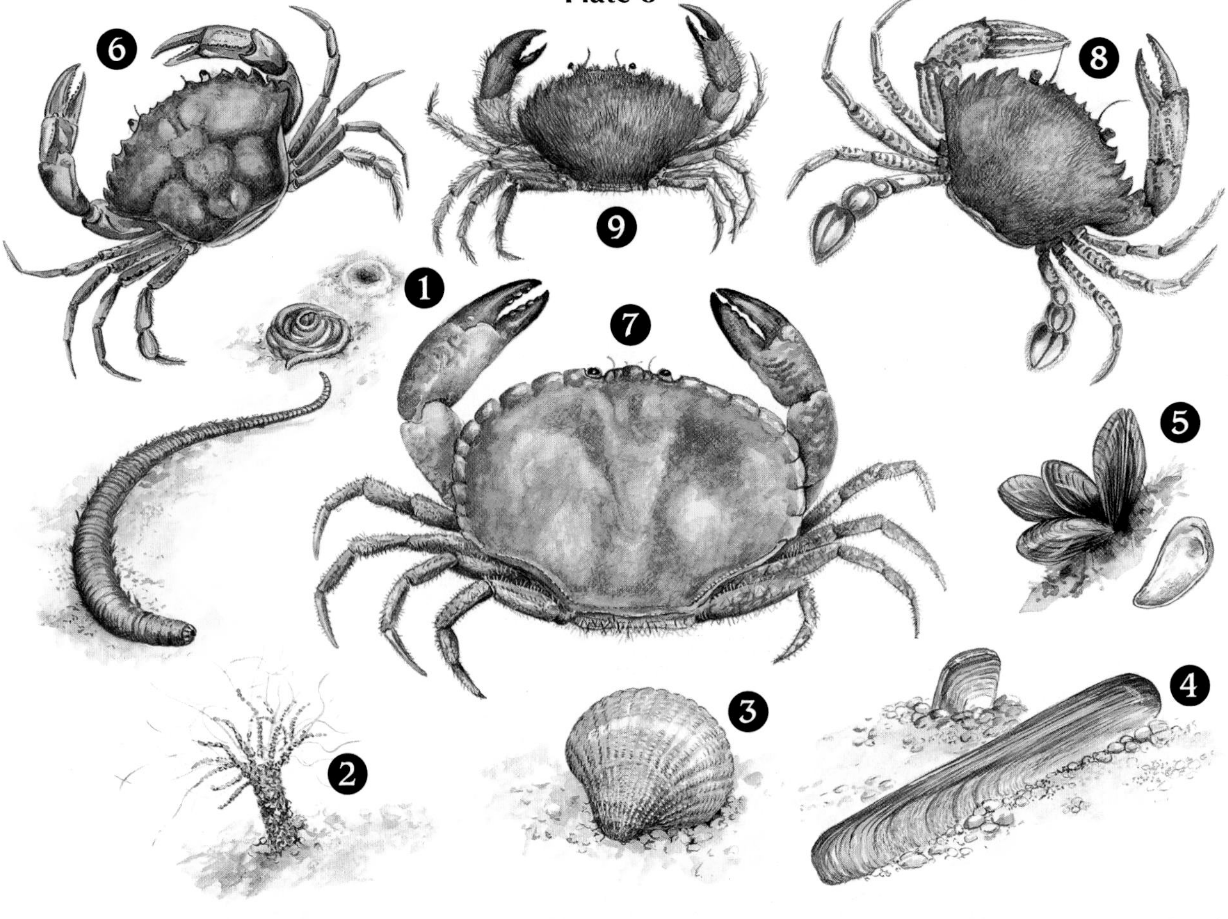